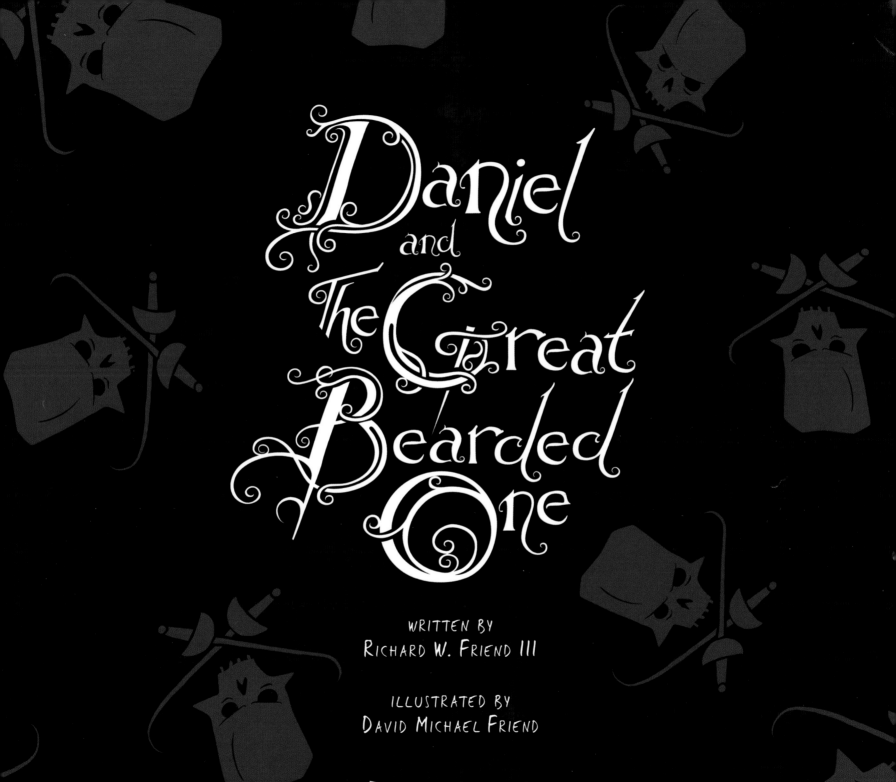

Daniel and The Great Bearded One

WRITTEN BY

RICHARD W. FRIEND III

ILLUSTRATED BY

DAVID MICHAEL FRIEND

MONDO

For my brother, David, who followed his heart and dream years ago and was good enough to invite me to be a part of it. And for those with a past and an eye on a different tomorrow.

—RWF

For those that have dreams of breaking free of their lives they live in, the universe is made up of multiple realities. The one you live in should be the one you are happy in.

— DMF

For information contact:
Mondo Publishing
980 Avenue of the Americas
New York, NY 10018

Visit our website at www.mondopub.com

Printed in China
07 08 09 PB 9 8 7 6 5 4 3 2 1
ISBN 1-59336-697-3
Design by David Michael Friend

Contents

Chapter 1

As dark and black as they come, the night looked like the end of a tunnel to nowhere.

For Daniel, this night — and the ones preceding it and those to follow — all seemed the same. Whether they were as clear as day, lit by a full moon, or, like tonight, covered in heavy fabric, it mattered not. It was just another end to another day in a long string that wound and curled its way toward the next tomorrow.

Daniel finished clearing off the tabletops in the inn where he spent his life. Just a young boy, he felt as if he had already lived a long life — a boring and joyless one at that — cleaning tables, making beds, and washing dishes. Sometimes he helped out in the kitchen by preparing meals for the guests. Not too long ago he had realized that the things he did today, he would do again and again in the days to come. The inn was small and cozy, with worn hardwood floors and a fireplace that should have been enough to warm his bones on a night like this. But it failed to melt away the thoughts he held this evening.

His parents had died when he was but three. He did not know anyone, and no one knew him. Mr. Franklin, the owner of the inn, was closest to him, but there was a distance that had never been bridged. Taking him in after the death of his parents, Mr. Franklin provided food and shelter in return for the chores that Daniel did, but little else.

Daniel was alone with his thoughts as he swept a broom across the floor that hours before had been danced and trampled on by people celebrating the end of the day. The guests had retired to their rooms, and Mr. Franklin had said goodnight.

By the dying embers of the fire and the few candles that remained lit, Daniel made his way to the door and looked out at the village.

Snow would be coming soon to the coast, if not tonight. The streets were silent, and the houses and storefronts dormant. Late at night, when the darkness was complete and the village was asleep, Daniel often feared that he was the only person on the planet still alive — that everyone else had gone away, and that he would never see anyone again.

To... e could not see much out in the streets — except ...ng he had never seen before.

Instruction
If not fit, pls cut the bands. It's ok to use without bands.

5

GOOD EVENING.

WHAT WOULD YOU LIKE?

SOME CACKLE-FRUIT AND MEAT WOULD BE FINE, YOUNG MAN.

AND FOR MY LUPINE COMPANION, IF YOU'D BE SO KIND AS TO BRING HIM A PLATE OF THE EVENING'S DINNER SCRAPS AND SOME WATER.

I'M NOT QUITE SURE THAT WE HAVE ANY CACKLE-FRUIT. IT SOUNDS EXOTIC, AND WE'RE MORE OF A MEAT-AND-POTATOES KIND OF PLACE.

OH I'M SURE YOU DO HAVE CACKLE-FRUIT.

IF I SIMPLY REFERRED TO THEM AS EGGS, COULD YOU ACCOMMODATE ME?

EMBARRASSED BY THE FACT THAT HE DID NOT KNOW THAT CACKLE-FRUIT AND EGGS WERE ONE AND THE SAME, DANIEL QUIETLY STOKED THE EMBERS IN THE FIREPLACE, THREW ON SOME FRESH LOGS, AND WAS SOON COOKING DINNER FOR HIS GUEST — WHO WAS NOW RATHER SUBDUED.

AFTER RUNNING SOME LEFTOVERS OUT TO THE WOLF, DANIEL CAME BACK IN AND NOTED THAT THE MAN WAS RUMMAGING THROUGH ONE OF THE MANY POUCHES BURIED WITHIN HIS LONG COAT.

HE TOOK OUT A SHEET OF PAPER, UNFOLDED IT, AND STUDIED IT IN THE FLICKERING CANDLELIGHT.

BESIDES YOU, WHO CALLS EGGS "CACKLE-FRUIT"?

OTHER PIRATES, THAT'S WHO.

I HAVE INDEED SAILED THE HIGH SEAS IN SEARCH OF ADVENTURE AND FORTUNE. I'VE FOUND PLENTY OF BOTH, ALONG WITH AN UNWANTED PIECE OF FAME ALONG THE WAY. BUT I PREFER TO THINK THAT I HAVE NOT ROBBED PEOPLE.
SURE, I'VE STOLEN MONEY FROM SHIPS AND OCEAN TOWNS, BUT I NEVER REALLY SAW OR KNEW THE PEOPLE IT BELONGED TO.
NOT KNOWING WHERE THE MONEY CAME FROM OR WHERE IT WAS GOING MADE IT A BIT EASIER TO SLEEP AT NIGHT. I DID IT TO LIVE AND SURVIVE. I KNEW NO OTHER WAY.
CLUCK
CLUCK
CLUCK
CLUCK
CLUCK
CLUCK
CLUCK
I MUST ADMIT, I DID GET A THRILL OUT OF FINDING TREASURE. THE HUNT AND ACQUISITION OF FINE JEWELRY WAS TERRIBLY HABIT-FORMING.
WRANGLE!
CLUCK
GET AWAY FROM THOSE HENS. THEY'RE NOT FOR YOU TO EAT!
IS THAT YOUR SHIP?

Chapter 5

DANIEL LOOKED AT THE BOAT'S WAKE AND SAW THAT THE SEA FOAMED PINK, CHURNING WITH THE BLOODY FOOD THAT HAD ATTRACTED THE INTEREST OF SOME INFAMOUS INHABITANTS OF THE SEA. NUMEROUS DORSAL FINS BROKE THE SURFACE AND SPED TOWARDS THE CAGES THAT ROGER HAD OPENED AND FILLED WITH TASTY TREATS FOR THE SHARKS.

GREAT WHITES! IT'S GOING TO BE A GOOD QUICK TRIP!

YOU SEE, DANIEL, SHARKS HAVE TO KEEP SWIMMING IN ORDER TO BREATHE. IN THE CONFINES OF THEIR CAGES, THEY CAN ONLY SWIM FORWARD.

WITH ME STEERING THE SHIP, AND THE SHARKS TRAPPED IN A FEEDING FRENZY, THEY'LL PROPEL THE SHIP ONWARD IN THE DIRECTION WE NEED TO GO.

CLINK

PEOPLE AND PLACES, HERE WE COME! HA!

DANIEL HOPED THAT ROGER KNEW WHERE THEY WERE GOING, THEN FELT ALL THE MORE FOOLISH FOR THE THOUGHT. HE WAS SURE THAT ROGER KNEW EXACTLY WHERE THEY WERE HEADED, AND HE SOON REALIZED THE SITUATION HE WAS IN. HE WAS ON A SHIP ROCKETING ACROSS THE OCEAN WITH A PIRATE WHO HAD A THING FOR SHARKS, WOLVES, AND RAVENS. DANIEL BEGAN HAVING SECOND THOUGHTS ABOUT COMING ALONG. BUT HIS THOUGHTS GREW BLURRY AND HIS EYES HEAVY AS THE HARD WORK OF ROWING CAUGHT UP WITH HIM. WRAPPING HIMSELF TIGHTLY IN HIS NEW COAT, HE CURLED UP IN A BALL AND FELL INTO A BLISSFUL SLEEP.

Chapter 4
The hours sailed away, and it was soon time for the adventure to begin.
Naptime is over, Daniel. See that lighthouse over there? That marks the first stop of our trip.
See ya, sharkies.
We'll leave the sail up. Although, I learned late in my career that sometimes it's best not to so boldly announce your arrival. My late education almost cost me my life, but learn I did.

APPROACHING UNDER THE COVER OF DARKNESS MAKES IT ALL THE MORE BETTER.

IT DOESN'T EVEN LOOK LIKE THERE'S ANYONE HERE TO SEE US. THIS PLACE LOOKS DEAD.

AN APPROPRIATE DESCRIPTION. WE MIGHT RUN INTO A FEW GHOSTS IF WE'RE LUCKY. THEY HAVE SOMETHING THAT IS RIGHTFULLY MINE. IN THE MORNING WE'LL GO GHOST HUNTING.

DID YOU SAY GHOSTS?

NO. YOU MUST BE HEARING THINGS.

I COULD HAVE SWORN YOU SAID GHOSTS.

ENOUGH TALK. LET'S FIND A PLACE TO REST FOR THE EVENING, GATHER SOME FIREWOOD, AND SET UP CAMP.

THEY FOUND A NICE SPOT BENEATH SOME ANCIENT TREES. A FEW STUBBORN LEAVES STILL CLUNG TO THE BRANCHES, NOT WILLING TO ADMIT THAT OLD MAN WINTER HAD COME. WRANGLE ENJOYED THE OPEN COUNTRYSIDE AND SOON FOUND PLENTY OF FOOD FOR DINNER.

THE RABBITS THAT HE BROUGHT BACK WERE OF PARTICULAR INTEREST TO ROGER, WHO SKEWERED A FEW AND LET THEM ROAST OVER THE FIRE.

EAT UP AND ENJOY. YOU'LL NEED PLENTY OF ENERGY FOR TOMORROW. WE WILL BE DOING A LITTLE SPELUNKING.

I HAVE NO IDEA WHAT THAT IS, BUT IT SOUNDS... IT ALMOST SOUNDS LIKE VOMITING.

NOT QUITE. WE WILL BE EXPLORING SOME CAVES. BUT YOU MIGHT SEE A THING OR THREE THAT WILL MAKE YOUR STOMACH UNEASY.

19

THE GIANT ARACHNID CATAPULTED AROUND THE ROOM, SPRAYING WEBBING ANYWHERE AND EVERYWHERE. THE WEBBING, AT FIRST COMING IN LONG, HEAVY STRINGS, SOON CAME FORTH IN SHEETS OF STICKINESS THAT THREATENED TO ENGULF WHATEVER THEY CAME INTO CONTACT WITH.

ROGER SAW TWO THINGS THAT MIGHT COME IN HANDY — THE ROPE OF WEBBING HANGING DOWN IN THE CENTER OF THE ROOM AND THE ROCK STRUCTURES ON THE ROOF OF THE CAVE.

HE DID NOT KNOW IF HE COULD CLIMB UP THE ROPE IN HIS ADVANCED YEARS, BUT DANIEL JUST MIGHT BE ABLE TO.

DANIEL! HAVE YOU EVER SWUNG A SWORD? IF NOT, YOU'RE GOING TO ON THIS DAY.

NEXT I'LL SWING THE WEB ROPE FROM THE GROUND TO GET YOUR MOMENTUM GOING. YOU'LL HAVE TO USE THE SWORD TO KNOCK ONE OF THOSE STALACTITES OFF OF THE CEILING.

IF I'M LUCKY, IT'LL FALL ON THE NOT—SO—ITSY—BITSY SPIDER AND KILL IT.

HERE'S THE PLAN: I'M GOING TO DISTRACT THE SPIDER WHILE YOU CLIMB UP THAT ROPE OF WEBBING THAT LEADS TO THE HOLE IN THE CEILING.

22

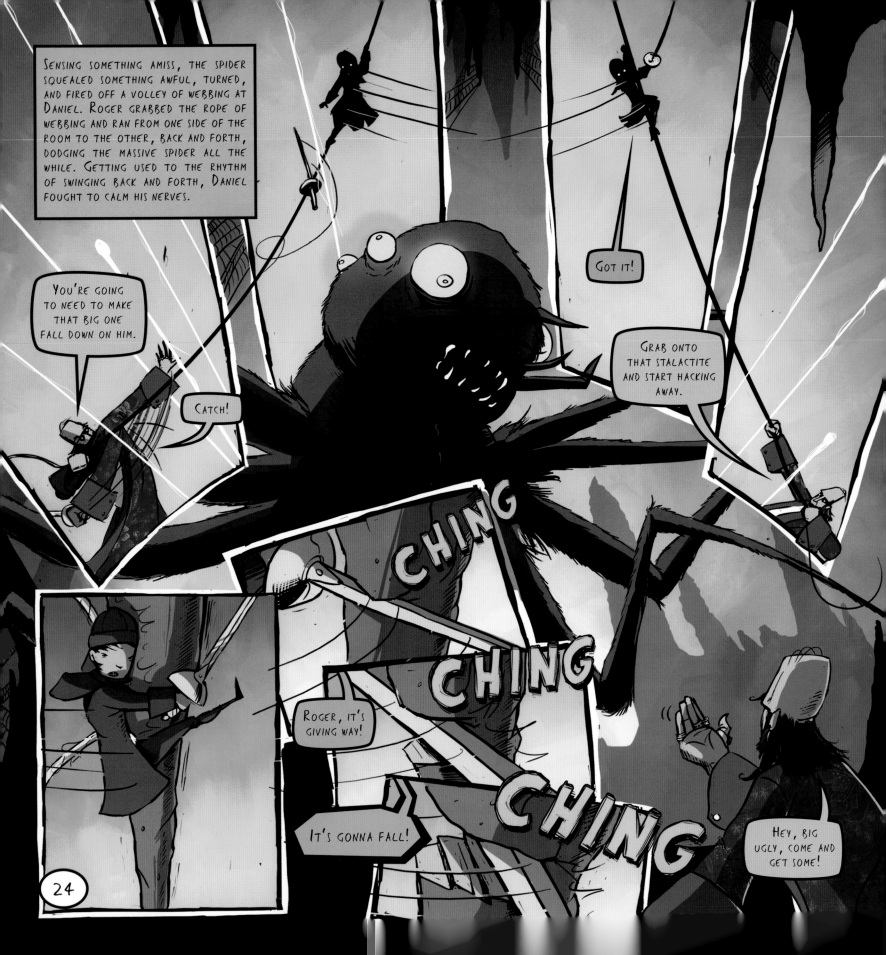

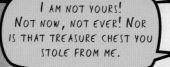

Because they're our clothes! As is everything else in this room!

Everything is ours!

I am not yours! Not now, not ever! Nor is that treasure chest you stole from me.

If you give it to me, my partner and I shall leave you in peace. If not... in pieces.

Oh, no, no, no, my bearded friend. We'll give you nothing, and you'll turn back and leave this room at your earliest possible convenience.

Actually, we suggest you leave right this very second.

Not a chance. I've come this far for what is mine.

The three Skeleteers retreated to a defensive position around the crown jewel of the room, an old wood and leather chest. The treasure chest sang to Roger and drew him forward.

Stay back, Daniel! This fight is mine and mine alone.

See this, Mr. Pirate? You can't have it. Nah, nah, nah, nah, na!

Chapter 7

BACK ON THE SHIP, ROGER ANTICIPATED SMOOTH SAILING AS THEIR ADVENTURE CONTINUED THE FOLLOWING DAY.

WHY NOW?

BECAUSE THE DECLARATION OF PARIS HAS BEEN SIGNED BY THE NATIONS OF THE WORLD, SO THOSE GOVERNMENTS THAT TOLERATED PIRACY ARE NO LONGER ABLE TO EMPLOY US.

I WILL NOW GET TO SEE MY FRIEND, AND THAT SHOULD BE THAT. I DON'T EXPECT ANY MORE SURPRISES.

WITH PIRATING NO LONGER AN OPTION, THE LAW CAN HUNT US DOWN. AND SINCE THE INVENTION OF STEAMBOATS, THEY NO LONGER NEED A STRONG WIND TO CHASE US. PIRACY AS I HAVE KNOWN IT IS JUST ABOUT FINISHED.

WHAT DOES THAT HAVE TO DO WITH YOUR FRIEND?

HE WON'T BE AROUND MUCH LONGER.

THAT DREADFUL DECLARATION QUIETED DANIEL, WHO TURNED HIS ATTENTION TO THE VILLAGES AND LAND THAT SWEPT PAST AS THE SHIP HEADED DOWN THE COAST. THE TWO RAVENS CONCENTRATED ON THE SKY BEHIND THE SHIP... AND ALSO THE TWO PARROTS TRAILING AT A DISTANCE.

35

That night, with the ship's sail lowered, they drifted towards shore. Waiting at the end of the dock was a sight that Daniel wished he had not seen. Hanging in an iron cage suspended from a wooden frame called a gibbet was a man. He was fully clothed and looked eerily like a younger version of Roger — at least to Daniel's eyes. But in the darkness, with only flickering fires from the barrels set below to illuminate him, it was tough to tell. That the man was dead there was no doubt.

What is that?

It's a not-so-gentle reminder to choose a different life for yourself.

Stopping in front of the man, Roger fell heavily to his knees.

The man you see before you was a young man with a good heart when I met him. I introduced him to the ways of pirates. I grew to trust him and respect him.

Over the years, that level of trust grew deeper, and he became my body double. He became my friend, and one of my greatest regrets.

What's a body double?

He'd go on missions for me that I felt were extremely dangerous, with a high risk of my being caught. He would dress like me and act like me. He became me.

The final mission I sent him on was his last. He was captured and brought to justice — in the eyes of those who decide it, at least.

Never did he deserve to be hung as a warning to others not to live the life of a pirate. With the Declaration of Paris serving to permanently outlaw pirates, there is no longer a need for public displays such as this. We're not going to wait and see what they will do with his body once they take it down. We're going to give my friend the proper burial that he deserves.

ROGER LOOKED UP AT THE HEAVY DARK SKY. THERE WAS NOT A STAR IN SIGHT. THE RAIN BOUNCED OFF HIS SKIN, CLEANSING THE TEARS FROM HIS FACE AND CLEARING HIS MIND FOR THE TASK AHEAD.

AREN'T YOU TIRED FROM THE PAST FEW DAYS? WE COULD REST AND BURY HIM IN THE MORNING.

WHY DIDN'T YOU DO THIS SOONER?

I WAS AFRAID I'D BE RECOGNIZED. PEOPLE MIGHT HAVE FOUND IT ODD TO SEE THE PIRATE THEY THOUGHT WAS HANGING AT THE END OF THE DOCK WALKING AROUND TOWN.

SINCE HIS PASSING, OUR RESEMBLANCE HAS LESSENED. I SHOULDN'T BE NOTICED. REGARDLESS, TONIGHT WE MAKE THINGS RIGHT.

I HAVE NOTICED MYSELF GROWING MORE AND MORE TIRED AS THE YEARS GO BY. TIRED OF A LOT OF THINGS. TIRED OF THINGS I'VE GROWN ACCUSTOMED TO DOING, AND TIRED OF NOT BEING ABLE TO CORRECT THINGS I'VE DONE.

BUT TONIGHT? TONIGHT I FEEL STRANGELY ALIVE. THE WEATHER IS PERFECT. THE GROUND IS SOFT FROM THE RAIN.

WRANGLE, STAND GUARD WHILE DANIEL AND I GRAB A BITE TO EAT AND GET SOME SUPPLIES.

BY THE TIME WE'RE BACK, THE TOWNSPEOPLE WILL BE IN BED, AND WE CAN DO WHAT WE HAVE TO DO IN PEACE AND QUIET.

CHAPTER 8

Upon entering the general store, Roger's mood lifted slightly. The aisles and shelves were stacked with anything and everything a person could ever need.

What can I do for you?

Two shovels, a coffin, and a cart with a harness. And one more thing. I need a key.

A key to what?

A key to anything. But it needs to look as close to this as possible.

Here's what we owe you for the goods... and a little extra for keeping quiet.

If anyone comes into the store asking about us, you never saw us.

He seemed rather shocked when you told him the harness was for a wolf.

Shrouded in silence, Roger led the way back to the dock — to Wrangle and his friend.

You're awfully quiet.

We've got work to do.

Daniel fastened the harness and cart to Wrangle, who offered no resistance. It was as if he understood the situation all too well.

Roger set out to free his friend. No one from town came to bother them. Maybe the driving rain continued to work in their favor by confining the noise to the dock. Or maybe nobody cared.

WITH ROGER'S FRIEND SAFELY IN THE COFFIN, WRANGLE LED THE GROUP OFF DOWN THE PATH.

WE'LL HEAD OFF THAT WAY AND SEE IF WE CAN FIND A SUITABLE BURIAL GROUND.

CONTINUING ON, WRANGLE SOON DISCOVERED A QUIET CLEARING FOR THE CEREMONY.

IDEAL CHOICE, WRANGLE. DANIEL, SHALL WE START THE DIG?

ROGER KEPT LOOKING BACK, WITH A WARY EYE, TO SEE IF ANYONE OR ANYTHING WAS FOLLOWING THEM. NOTHING OR NOBODY WAS THERE — AT LEAST AS FAR AS HE COULD TELL.

ROGER DUG WITH PASSION AND FURY. DANIEL TRIED TO KEEP PACE SO AS NOT TO DISAPPOINT ROGER. THE SOFT EARTH OFFERED LITTLE RESISTANCE TO THEIR SHOVELS. PILES OF DIRT BEGAN TO BUILD UP AS THE HOLE DEEPENED AND THEY SOON HAD THE GRAVE PREPARED.

GENTLY AND CAREFULLY, ROGER AND DANIEL LOWERED THE COFFIN INTO THE EARTH.

MAY THIS TREE GROW WITH YOU AS YOU ARE FINALLY ABLE TO ENJOY THE NEXT STAGE OF YOUR LIFE. MAY ITS LEAVES FALL SOFTLY ON YOU IN AUTUMN AND WARM YOU IN WINTER. COME SPRING AND SUMMER, MAY IT GROW TALL AND SHIELD YOU FROM THE HARSHNESS THAT LIFE CAN OFFER — FAR BETTER THAN I DID.

I HOPE THAT IF AND WHEN WE MEET AGAIN, YOU'LL UNDERSTAND THAT I MEANT YOU NO HARM. I HOPE YOU WON'T TURN A COLD SHOULDER TO ME. NOW, REST MY FRIEND. PLEASE REST.

MARY BONNIE SHUDDERED AND SHOOK AS THE AIR GREW ELECTRIC WITH KINETIC ENERGY. ELECTRIC BLUE LIGHTNING EXPLODED AROUND AND THROUGH HER...

...AS BEFORE ROGER AND DANIEL'S VERY EYES, SHE SPLIT INTO TWO SEPARATE BEINGS. MASQUERADING AS MEN ONCE AGAIN, THE TWO APPEARED AS THE PIRATES THAT HAD LONG AGO SAILED ON ROGER'S SHIP.

ROGER SPURRED HIS HORSE ON AS SHOTS OF ICE WHIZZED PAST HIS HEAD. HE WAS NOT AT ALL INTERESTED IN FINDING OUT WHAT MIGHT OCCUR IF BONNIE SHOULD HAPPEN TO RUN HIM DOWN.

YOU CAN RUN LONG AND HARD, ROGER, BUT YOU CAN'T HIDE. THAT KEY — AND THE SECRET TO WHAT IT UNLOCKS — WILL BE MINE.

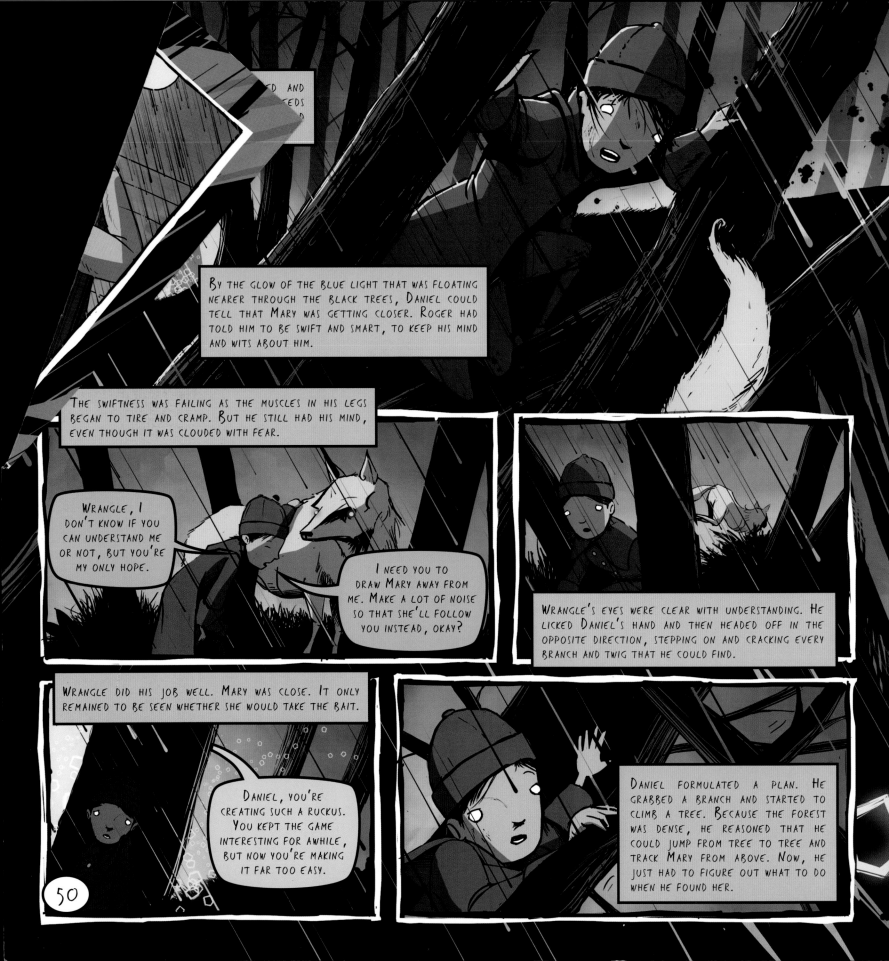

...ED AND
...EDS
...

By the glow of the blue light that was floating nearer through the black trees, Daniel could tell that Mary was getting closer. Roger had told him to be swift and smart, to keep his mind and wits about him.

The swiftness was failing as the muscles in his legs began to tire and cramp. But he still had his mind, even though it was clouded with fear.

Wrangle, I don't know if you can understand me or not, but you're my only hope.

I need you to draw Mary away from me. Make a lot of noise so that she'll follow you instead, okay?

Wrangle's eyes were clear with understanding. He licked Daniel's hand and then headed off in the opposite direction, stepping on and cracking every branch and twig that he could find.

Wrangle did his job well. Mary was close. It only remained to be seen whether she would take the bait.

Daniel, you're creating such a ruckus. You kept the game interesting for awhile, but now you're making it far too easy.

Daniel formulated a plan. He grabbed a branch and started to climb a tree. Because the forest was dense, he reasoned that he could jump from tree to tree and track Mary from above. Now, he just had to figure out what to do when he found her.

MEANWHILE, ROGER LET THE HORSE RUN AS FAST AS IT COULD AS THE GROUND LEVELED OFF. BONNIE WAS HOT ON HIS HEELS. IN THE DISTANCE, ROGER SAW THE PATH ANGLING TOWARDS THE SEASIDE AND UP INTO THE TALL, ROCKY HILLS. PUSHING THE HORSE EVEN FASTER, HE SPED ON.

BUT ROGER KNEW HE NEEDED TO DO SOMETHING MORE. HE COULD NOT KEEP ON RUNNING FOREVER.

Meanwhile over in the rocky hills, thoughts of Daniel kept Roger going. He had put Daniel in harm's way, and he was not happy about that. Earlier in their journey together, he would not have cared. But now he found his feelings had changed.

Roger's thoughts returned to the supernatural being who was aggressively pursuing him. Racing forward he saw that the path ahead was coated in ice.

All that time spent tracking down the key and finally burying his friend, and in the end, it seemed, he was not going to be able to complete his journey after all.

Bonnie would not give up at any cost and failed to slow down on the slick, icy trail. Roger sensed the end coming. His horse's balance faltered, and it started to slip and slide down the path. All Roger's mind could process was the ocean that lay far, far below at the bottom of the icy cliff upon which he rode.

Then, as is often the case in life, an opportunity presented itself.

AND ROGER JUMPED AT THE CHANCE!

BONNIE, HOWEVER, WAS NOT SO LUCKY. HER RECKLESS WAYS FINALLY CAUGHT UP WITH HER.

BYE-BYE, BONNIE.

GOT ANY STRENGTH LEFT TO CARRY ME BACK? I'VE GOT A FRIEND TO FIND.

Chapter 10

The next day found Roger and Daniel back aboard the ship, heading south under sunny skies. The sharks, back for the final leg of the journey, combined with a strong wind, made the trip quicker than expected. But still there was much idle time to pass.

There was plenty for them to do to fill the days, though. Roger had Wrangle to take care of. He cleaned his wounded leg and made a splint out of wood that would keep as much weight and pressure off of it as possible. Comfort and love would get Wrangle back to his old self, of that Roger was sure.

I've heard of pirates with wooden legs, but I never knew of a pirate's pet to have one.

How's your arm, Roger? That Skeleteer's sword sliced into it pretty deep.

It's fine. Thank you for asking.

I haven't had many people throughout my life ask me how I was doing. Not that I gave anyone much of a chance. Except for Arthur. That was the name of the friend we buried last night.

How did you and Arthur get to be friends?

I don't recall. I don't think you ever set out to become friends with someone. Friendship just happens. It's something that you want to trap and bottle and then drink from often. You've got to enjoy it. Because before you know it, your friend disappears, and you're alone.

THE SUN WAS SHINING BRILLIANT AND HOT WHEN THEY AWOKE. CLOTHES WERE BARELY NECESSARY IN THE HUMID AIR THAT CLUNG TO THEIR SKIN AND WOULD NOT LET GO. ROGER LOOKED WILD AND FREE, LIKE A MAN SOON TO BE RELIEVED OF THE BURDEN OF HIS PAST.

A WORD OF ADVICE TO EACH OF YOU. YOU'LL SEE LOTS OF STRANGE ANIMALS IN THIS JUNGLE. DON'T BITE THEM, AND THEY WON'T BITE YOU.

ROGER, DANIEL, AND WRANGLE HEADED DEEPER INTO THE THICK JUNGLE. MONKEYS RACED FROM TREE TO TREE, SNAKES SLITHERED OFF INTO THE DAMP DARKNESS, AND ALL SORTS OF WILDLIFE CAME OUT TO TRACK THE TRIO.

GGGGGRROAAWRL

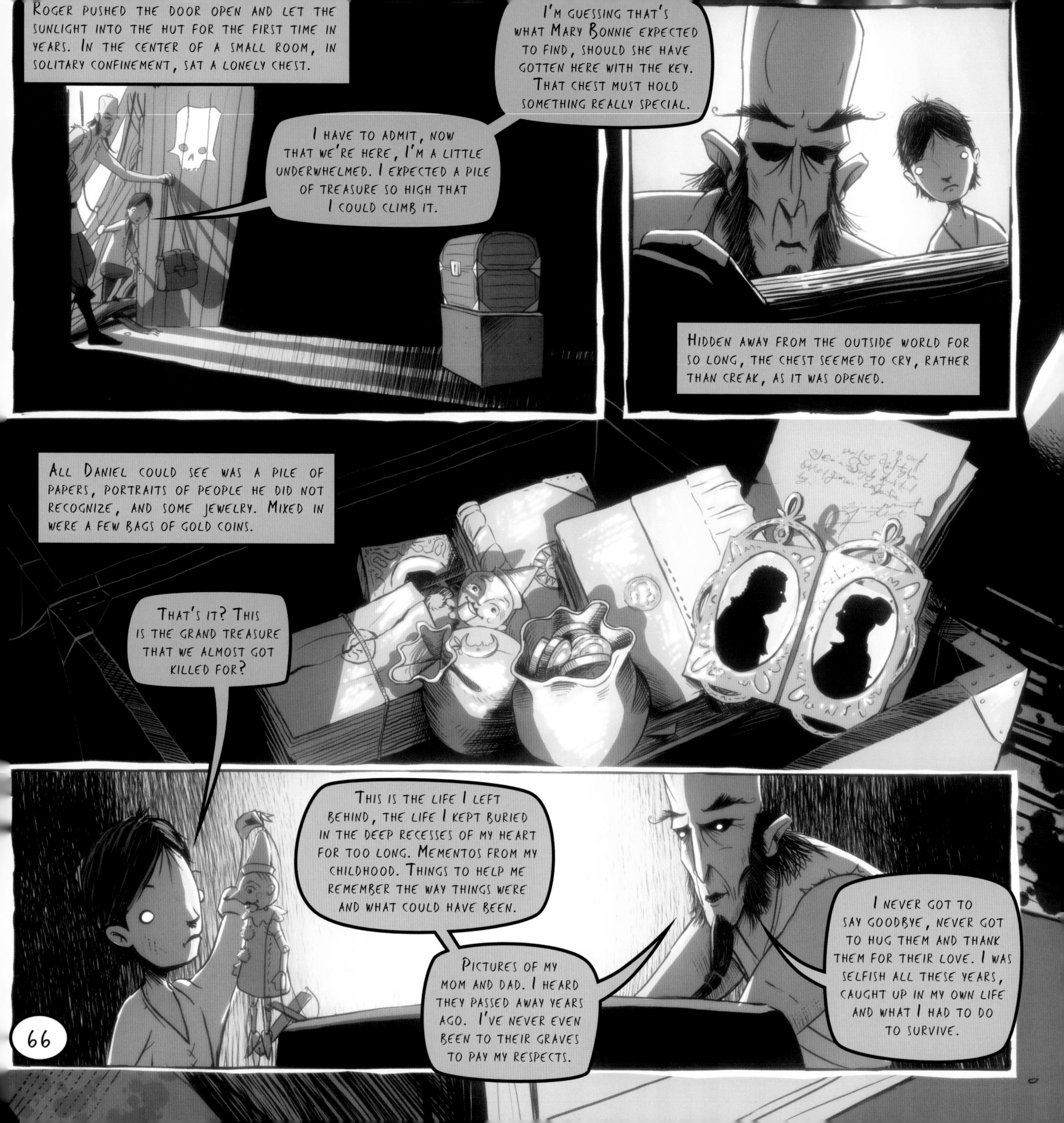
ROGER PUSHED THE DOOR OPEN AND LET THE SUNLIGHT INTO THE HUT FOR THE FIRST TIME IN YEARS. IN THE CENTER OF A SMALL ROOM, IN SOLITARY CONFINEMENT, SAT A LONELY CHEST.
I HAVE TO ADMIT, NOW THAT WE'RE HERE, I'M A LITTLE UNDERWHELMED. I EXPECTED A PILE OF TREASURE SO HIGH THAT I COULD CLIMB IT.
I'M GUESSING THAT'S WHAT MARY BONNIE EXPECTED TO FIND, SHOULD SHE HAVE GOTTEN HERE WITH THE KEY. THAT CHEST MUST HOLD SOMETHING REALLY SPECIAL.
HIDDEN AWAY FROM THE OUTSIDE WORLD FOR SO LONG, THE CHEST SEEMED TO CRY, RATHER THAN CREAK, AS IT WAS OPENED.
ALL DANIEL COULD SEE WAS A PILE OF PAPERS, PORTRAITS OF PEOPLE HE DID NOT RECOGNIZE, AND SOME JEWELRY. MIXED IN WERE A FEW BAGS OF GOLD COINS.
THAT'S IT? THIS IS THE GRAND TREASURE THAT WE ALMOST GOT KILLED FOR?
THIS IS THE LIFE I LEFT BEHIND, THE LIFE I KEPT BURIED IN THE DEEP RECESSES OF MY HEART FOR TOO LONG. MEMENTOS FROM MY CHILDHOOD. THINGS TO HELP ME REMEMBER THE WAY THINGS WERE AND WHAT COULD HAVE BEEN.
PICTURES OF MY MOM AND DAD. I HEARD THEY PASSED AWAY YEARS AGO. I'VE NEVER EVEN BEEN TO THEIR GRAVES TO PAY MY RESPECTS.
I NEVER GOT TO SAY GOODBYE, NEVER GOT TO HUG THEM AND THANK THEM FOR THEIR LOVE. I WAS SELFISH ALL THESE YEARS, CAUGHT UP IN MY OWN LIFE AND WHAT I HAD TO DO TO SURVIVE.

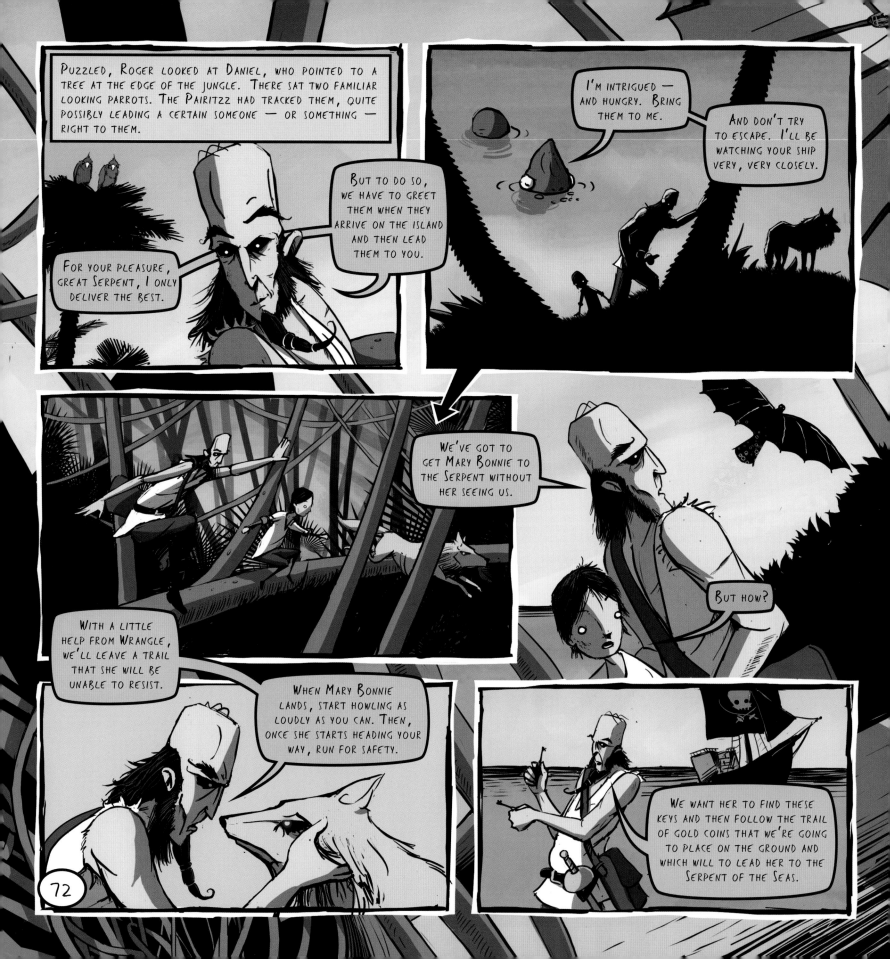

KAAWF

KAAWF
KAAWF